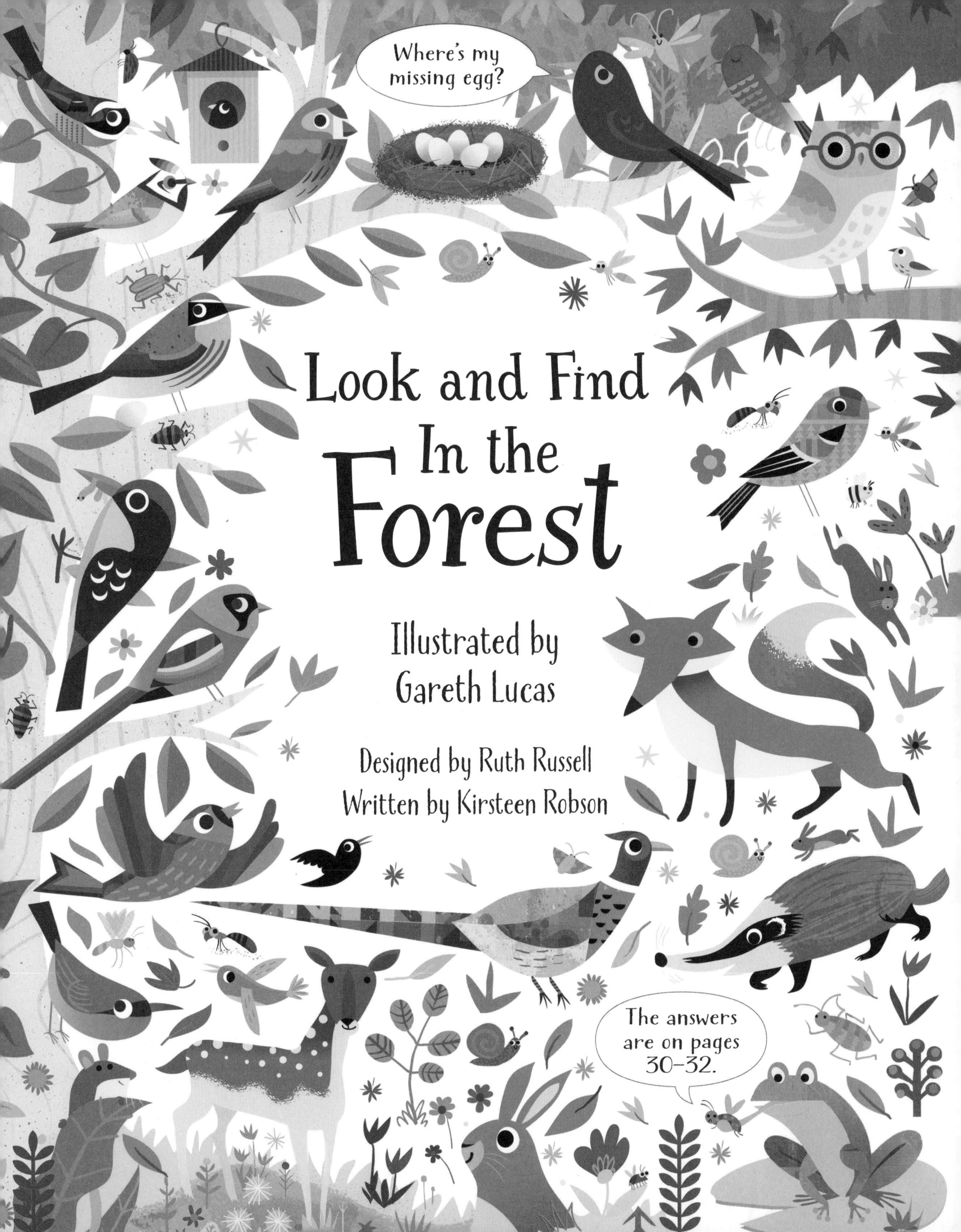

Find two bats hanging from branches.
Which wolf has a toothy grin?
Who is howling at the moon?

14

ANSWERS

Cover

There are 2 squirrels.

1

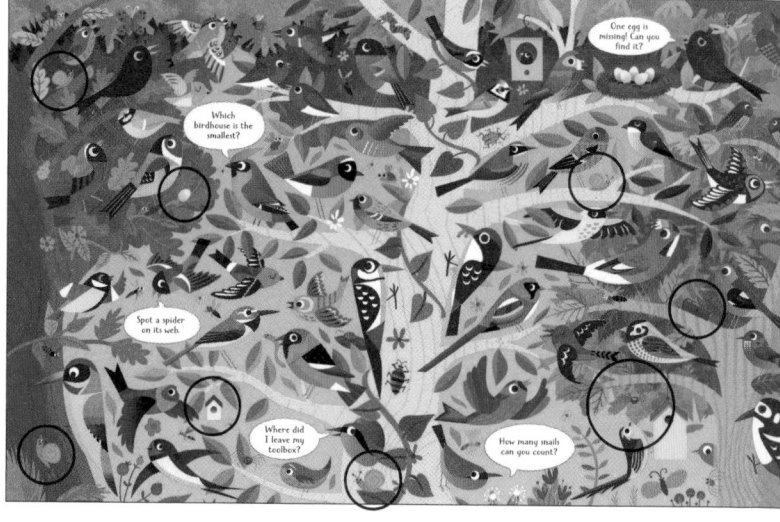

There are 7 creatures wearing sunhats.   2-3

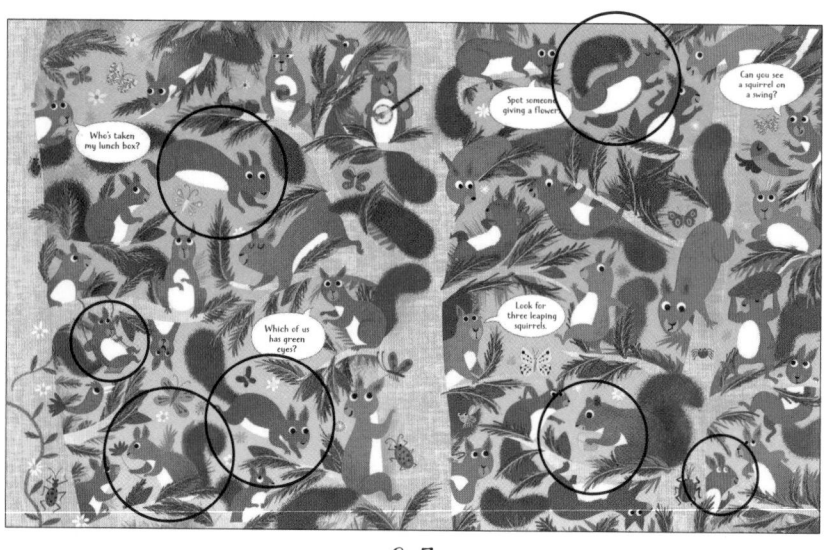

There are 4 snails.   4-5

6-7

8-9

30

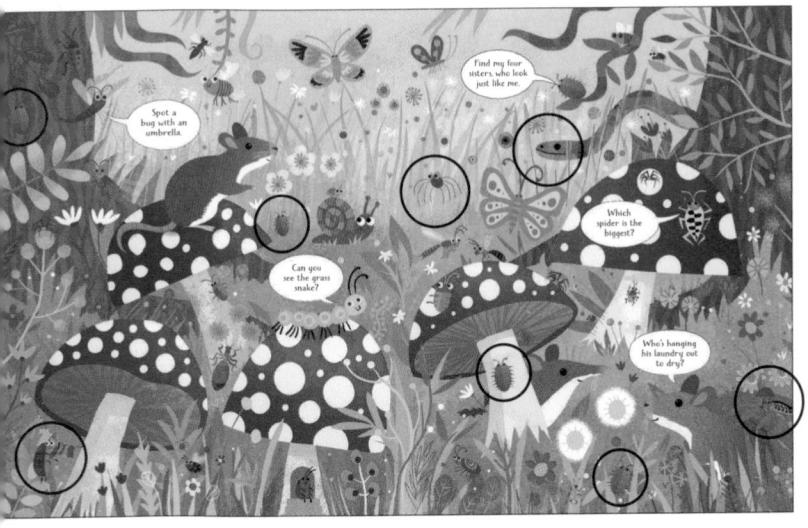

10-11

5 birds have found something to eat. 12-13

14-15

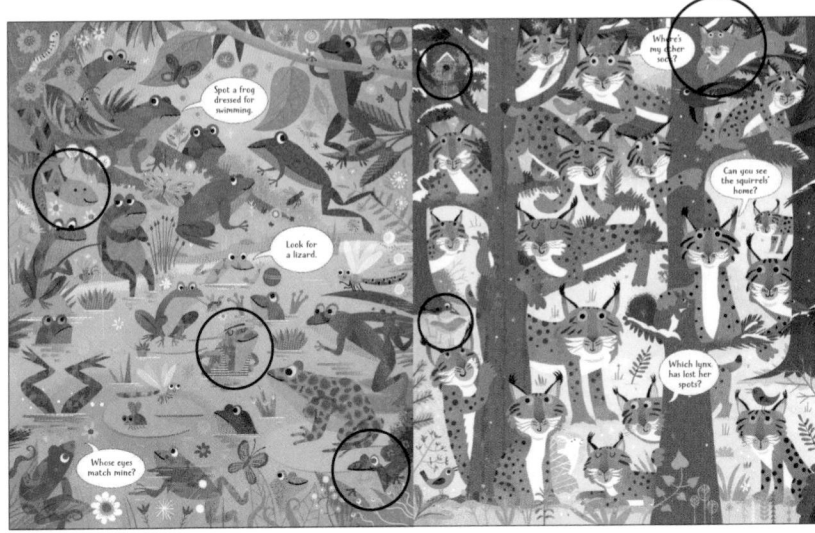

16-17

18-19

There are 6 fish. 20-21

22-23   The fox might catch 3 rabbits.

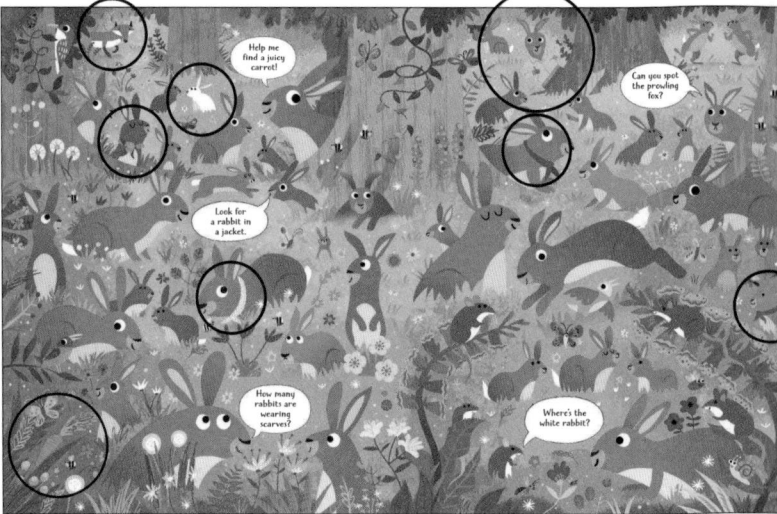

There are 4 rabbits wearing scarves.   24-25

There are 9 hedgehogs.   26-27

28-29